BUS STOP

MUSIC FOR LIVING SERIES

Companion Books for Teacher's Book One:

"I Like the City" . . . "I Like the Country"

I Like the City

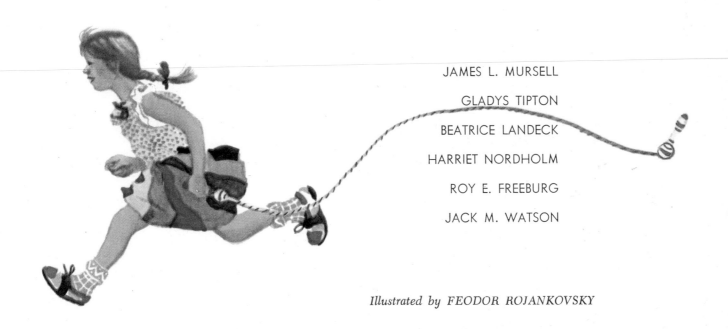

JAMES L. MURSELL

GLADYS TIPTON

BEATRICE LANDECK

HARRIET NORDHOLM

ROY E. FREEBURG

JACK M. WATSON

Illustrated by FEODOR ROJANKOVSKY

Silver Burdett Company

MORRISTOWN, N. J.   CHICAGO   DALLAS

NEW YORK   SAN FRANCISCO   ATLANTA

Acknowledgments

Grateful acknowledgment is made to the following poets, folklorists, and publishers for the use of song and poetry material:

Marcette Chute for the poem, "Sliding," from RHYMES ABOUT THE CITY, published by The Macmillan Company.

The John Day Company Inc. for the poem "Stop-Go," from I LIKE AUTOMOBILES, copyright 1931 by Dorothy Walter Baruch.

Eleanor Farjeon for "Music" ("Hurdy-Gurdy") from POEMS FOR CHILDREN, published by J. B. Lippincott Co.

Harper & Brothers for the poem, "In the City," from I LIVE IN A CITY by James S. Tippett. Copyright 1927 by Harper & Brothers.

Ruby Terrill Lomax for "The Wind Blew East" from OUR SINGING COUNTRY, published by The Macmillan Company.

The Macmillan Company for "Hello, Somebody" from SHANTY MEN AND SHANTY BOYS by William Doerflinger.

Theodore Presser Co., copyright owner, for "When the Train Comes Along," from AMERICAN NEGRO SONGS by John W. Work.

The Texas Folklore Society for "Toodala," from TOODALA by Helen Gates.

Young People's Records and Marion Abeson for "Giddy-ap Pony," from "Who Wants a Ride," Young People's Record 806.

I love the city, I find many things to do,
I play in the park, I go to the zoo.
In my apartment I have toys and games,
And so many picture books
I can't tell their names.
I stand at my window, I see a whole fleet
Of streetcars and taxis and trucks in the street.

            —JAMES S. TIPPETT

Contents

HELLO, SOMEBODY

ENGLISH SEA CHANTEY

Hel - lo, Some - bod - y, hel - lo!

There's Some - bod - y knock - ing at the gar - den gate;

Hel - lo, Some - bod - y hel - lo!

There's Some - bod - y knock - ing at the gar - den gate;

Somebody has come to visit the city.

Hel - lo, Some - bod - y, hel - lo!

1

City streets are crowded with big trucks.

The horns on big trucks say:

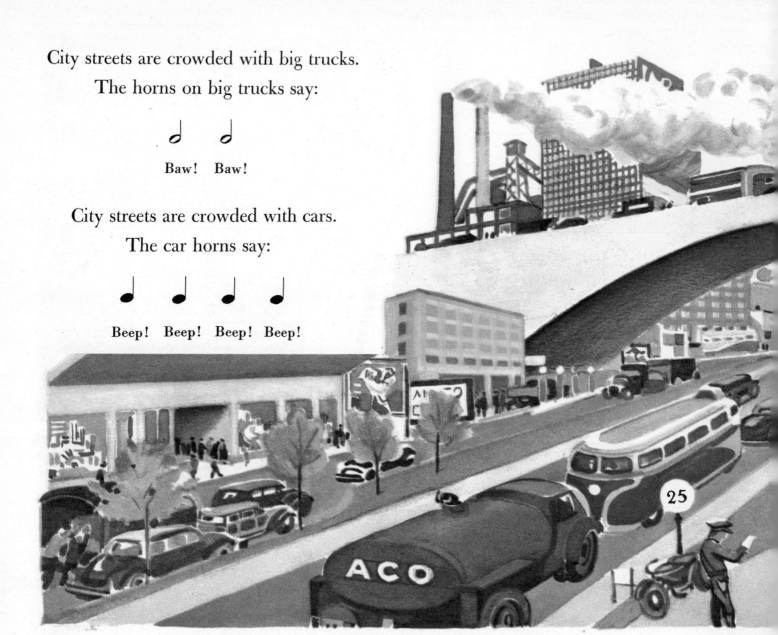

Baw! Baw!

City streets are crowded with cars.

The car horns say:

Beep! Beep! Beep! Beep!

City streets are crowded with buses, too.

The buses are crowded with people.

Everybody in the city hurries—hurries—hurries.

3

STOP-GO

WORDS BY DOROTHY BARUCH
MUSIC BY ARTHUR EDWARDS

All of the cars In a row Wait to

go While the sig nal says: STOP.

The red light is on.
The red light means

STOP ✔ ✔ ✔
STOP ✔ ✔ ✔
STOP ✔ ✔ ✔

4

Bells ring Ting - a - ling! Red light's gone! Green light's on!

Horns blow! And the row— Starts to GO.

The green light is on.
The green light means

GO
GO
GO

Some children in the city
live high up in apartment houses.

6

When they go to school in the morning,
                    they push a button.   Bzzzzz...
The elevator comes to get them.

The elevator man says:

"Go - ing   down!"

When they come home from school,
          the elevator takes them upstairs.

"Go - ing   up!"

BIG MACHINES

WORDS AND MUSIC BY N. VACIO

Cree - ee - k! Cree - ee - k!

That's the way it starts to work.

Cree - ee - k! Cree - ee - k!

Down it comes to pick up its load;

Big claws, big claws, My big crane. ___

Workmen are building a skyscraper
in a big city lot.

The big crane starts to work:

Cree -   ee -   k!

It bends down low.
Its big claws pick up a heavy load,
        and swing . . swing . . swing . .
The load is carried to the place
        where the men are working.

Swing . . swing . . bend . . stop,
Lift . . swing . . swing . . drop.

9

In warm weather
the ice cream man comes
down the city streets.

Somebody hears his car play a tune:

On the corner Tony sells his papers:

"Eve - ning pa - pers! Five cents a cop - y"

11

There are many stores on city streets.

Everybody knows the grocery man,
the fruit man, the shoemaker, and the butcher.

12

DO YOU KNOW?

SINGING GAME

Oh, do you know the gro-cery man,

The gro-cery man, the gro-cery man;

Oh, do you know the gro-cery man

Who lives a-cross the street?

In the city, children play street games.

They sing a little tune

as the skipping rope goes around and around,

and the children in the block run in and out in turn.

TOODALA

PLAY-PARTY GAME FROM TEXAS

Might - y pret - ty mo - tion, too - da - la, too - da - la, too - da - la,

Might - y pret - ty mo - tion, too - da - la, too - da - la - la, la - dy.

15

THE WIND BLEW EAST

FOLK SONG FROM THE BAHAMAS

Oh, the wind blew east, Whoooo!
(imitate wind)

The wind blew — west, Whoooo!
(imitate wind)

The wind blew the sun-shine Right down to town.

16

Sometimes the wind brings rain.
Sometimes it brings sunshine.

The wind blows up and down the city streets.
It blows around the tall buildings.

Whoooo! _____

The fire alarm rings in the city firehouse.

Ding ding ding

Ding ding ding

The firemen slide down a pole.
They put on fire hats and boots.
They jump on the fire engine.

The fire engine rushes down the street.

Wah

The fire siren tells people to get out of the way.

HURDY-GURDY

WORDS BY ELEANOR FARJEON
MUSIC BY ERNEST GOLD

Can you dance? I love to dance! Mu - sic is my hap - py chance.

Mu - sic play - ing in the street Gets in - to my hands and feet.

On a bright sunny day,
  children dance on city streets.
The music of the hurdy-gurdy plays,
  as a little monkey holds out his hat
  for pennies.

20

The city streets need many repairs.
  Two men work together
    to loosen the hard pavement.

Down goes one sledge hammer.
The other swings up . .
    Strike . . swing up . .
    Strike . . swing up . .

One goes up.
The other goes down.
    Strike . . swing up . .
    Strike . . swing up . .
Their hammers ring:

Zing   Zing   Zing   Zing

Children play in the city park
after school.

They climb on the jungle gym.
They go up and down
on the swing.

SLIDING

WORDS BY MARCETTE CHUTE
MUSIC BY ERNEST GOLD

Down the slide we ride, we ride. Round we run, and then,

Up we pop to reach the top, Down we come a - gain.

Somebody tries the slide.

Up the ladder:

Down the slide:

23

The park comes in flower in the spring.
    Tulip bulbs wake up from sleep
    and begin to stir.

    They push and push.

They push their way through the soil
    and slowly, slowly,
    peek out above the ground.

    Up, up come the leaves.
    Up, up comes a tiny bud.

    Little by little the buds open
    and hold their faces to the sun.

Somebody sits on the bench and watches the pigeons.

THREE BLUE PIGEONS

AMERICAN FOLK SONG

1. Three blue pi - geons sit - ting on the wall.

Three blue pi - geons— sit - ting on the wall.

Spoken: One flew away.
O-o-oh!

2. Two blue pigeons sitting on the wall.
Two blue pigeons sitting on the wall.
Another flew away.
O-o-o-o-oh!

3. One blue pigeon sitting on the wall.
One blue pigeon sitting on the wall.
And the third flew away!
O-o-o-o-o-o-oh!

4. No blue pigeons sitting on the wall.
   No blue pigeons sitting on the wall.
   One flew back.
   Whee-ee-ee!

5. One blue pigeon sitting on the wall.
   One blue pigeon sitting on the wall.
   Another flew back.
   Whee-ee-ee-ee!

6. Two blue pigeons sitting on the wall.
   Two blue pigeons sitting on the wall.
   And the third flew back!
   Whee-ee-ee-ee-ee-ee!

7. Three blue pigeons sitting on the wall.
   Three blue pigeons sitting on the wall.

27

There are ponies in the park—

   black ponies, white ponies, and red ponies.

The red pony trots like this:

The white pony gallops like this:

GIDDY-AP PONY

WORDS BY MARION ABESON
MUSIC BY CHARITY BAILEY

Gid - dy - ap po - ny, Clop, clop, clop, clop;

Gid - dy - ap po - ny, Lift that knee.

Gid - dy - ap po - ny, Clop, clop, clop, clop;

Gid - dy - ap po - ny, Trot with me.

In the park there is a zoo.

THE LION

ROGER
NEW YORK CITY SCHOOL

Once there was a lion,

He walked up and down the cage.

He walked up and down, and up and down,

And up and down the cage._____

30

Big children and little children
  watch the animals walk up and down,
  up and down
  in their cages.

The city is close to a river.

Big ships come up the river
    to bring food to people in the city.

Little tugboats work in the river.
    They pull barges up and down.
    They push big ships into dock
    and nose them out to sea again.

LITTLE TUGBOAT

GROUP OF CHILDREN
NEW YORK CITY SCHOOL

Oh, the stump-y lit-tle tug-boat, Works in the riv-er.

Pull-ing bar-ges up and down, up and down. ___

WHEN THE TRAIN COMES ALONG

AMERICAN FOLK SONG

When the train comes a- long,— when the train comes a-long,—

I'll   meet you at   the sta - tion when the train comes a - long.

34

Somebody is ready to leave the city.
"Goodbye, Somebody!"

Good - bye, Some-bod-y, good - bye!

Somebody's daddy will be at the station
when the train comes along.

Somebody is at home in bed,
  thinking of all the city children
  who are in bed, too.

ALL NIGHT, ALL DAY

NEGRO SPIRITUAL

All   night,   all _____ day,

An - gels watch - ing o - ver me, my Lord, __

All   night,   all _____ day,

An - gels watch - ing o - ver me. ____